Perpetual
Disappointments
Diary

Nick Asbury

BOXTREE

First published 2014 by Asbury & Asbury

This edition published 2017 by Boxtree
an imprint of Pan Macmillan
20 New Wharf Road, London N1 9RR
Associated companies throughout the world
www.panmacmillan.com

ISBN 978-0-7522-6654-1

Copyright © Asbury & Asbury

asburyandasbury.com

The right of Asbury & Asbury to be identified as the
authors of this work has been asserted by them in accordance
with the Copyright, Designs and Patents Act 1988.

'Bank Insecurity Questions' first published by *McSweeney's Internet Tendency*

Thanks to Jim Sutherland and everyone who has helped
make this diary what it unfortunately is.

9 8 7 6 5 4 3 2 1

A CIP catalogue record for this book is available from the British Library.

Printed in China

Visit **www.panmacmillan.com** to read more about all our books
and to buy them. You will also find features, author interviews and
news of any author events, and you can sign up for e-newsletters
so that you're always first to hear about our new releases.

1.

2.

3.

4.

- This diary is suitable for use any year – it doesn't matter.
- Write a 'M' for Monday on the first Monday of the year, then count seven days forward and write another 'M'. Keep doing this.

Personal Information

Name

Address

Telephone

Mobile

Email

Previous Convictions

Known Medical Conditions

Next Of Kin

Bin Night

If this diary has been lost, on no account start an inspirational social media campaign to find its owner.

Bank Insecurity Questions

Which parts of your body are you most uncomfortable with?

When you chose that outfit this morning, how did you think you looked?

How does it feel watching your friends become successful?

On a scale of 1 to 10, how much does your birth father look like you?

Could a stranger theoretically have a copy of your front door key?

Are you sure about your answers so far?

What do you think your partner says to other people about your sex life?

Do you ever wonder what people think of your speaking voice?

Do the rumours going round lately concern you?

Why do dogs look at you like that?

Conversion Factors

Length

1 millimetre (mm)		0.0394 in
1 centimetre (cm)	10 mm	0.3937 in
1 metre (m)	100 cm	1.0936 yd
1 kilometre (km)	1 000 m	0.6214 mile
1 miss		1 mile

Area

1 sq cm (cm²)	100 mm²	0.1550 in²
1 sq metre (m²)	10 000 cm²	1.1960 yd²
1 sq kilometre (km²)	100 hectares	0.3861 mile²
1 sq meal (ml²)		1 Pot Noodle

Mass

1 milligram (mg)		0.0154 grain
1 gram (g)	1 000 mg	0.0353 oz
1 metric carat	0.2 g	3.0865 grains
1 kilogram (kg)	1 000 g	2.2046 lb
1 tonne (t)	1 000 kg	0.9842 ton
1 damp squib		0.1345 lead balloon

Capacity

1 litre (l)	1 dm³	1.76 pt
1 hectolitre (hl)	100 l	21.998 gal
1 glass		½ empty

Temperature

Temperature °C	°F	Description
100	212	scalding
40	104	cup-a-soup
39	102.2	worrying fever
30	86	dreaded sunny day
21	70	room temperature
10	50	bedsit temperature
0	32	brass monkeys
-1	30.2	frosty glance
-18	0	icy stare
-40	-40	cold day in hell

Length

1 inch (in)		2.54 cm
1 foot (ft)	12 in	0.3048 m
1 yard (yd)	3 ft	0.9144 m
1 mile	1 760 yd	1.6093 km
1 stare	1 000 yd	0.9144 km

Area

1 sq inch (in^2)		6.4516 cm^2
1 sq foot (ft^2)	144 in^2	0.0929 m^2
1 sq yard (yd^2)	9 ft^2	0.8361 m^2
1 acre	4 840 yd^2	4 046.9 m^2
1 sq mile (mile^2)	640 acres	2.590 km^2
1 sq peg (peg^2)		1 round hole

Mass

1 ounce (oz)	437.5 grains	28.35 g
1 pound (lb)	16 oz	0.4536 kg
1 stone	14 lb	6.3503 kg
1 hundredweight (cwt)	112 lb	50.802 kg
1 ton	20 cwt	1.016 t
1 deadweight	1 millstone	0.5 albatross

Capacity

1 fluid ounce (fl oz)		28.413 ml
1 pint (pt)	20 fl oz	0.5683 l
1 gallon (gal)	8 pt	4.546 l
1 Kestrel Super (pt)		9.0% vol

Useful Phrases
English, French, German, Spanish and Mandarin

I have lost my passport

F: J'ai perdu mon passeport

G: Ich habe meinen Pass verloren

S: He perdido el pasaporte

M: 我丢了护照

I am on the wrong plane

F: Je me suis trompé d'avion

G: Ich bin im falschen Flugzeug

S: Me he equivocado de avión

M: 我上错了飞机

I have destroyed my hire car

F: J'ai accidenté ma voiture de location

G: Ich habe mein Mietauto kaputt gefahren

S: He estrellado el coche de alquiler

M: 我毁掉了租来的车子

I do not have health insurance

F: Je n'ai pas d'assurance maladie

G: Ich habe keine Krankenversicherung

S: No tengo seguro médico

M: 我没有医疗保险

When will the construction work finish?

F: Quand est-ce que les travaux de construction seront-ils finis?

G: Wann sind die Bauarbeiten vorbei?

S: ¿Cuando acabarán las obras?

M: 这工程什么时候竣工?

Can I book an alarm call for midday?

F: Puis-je vous demander de me reveiller à midi?

G: Kann ich bitte einen Weckanruf für mittags buchen?

S: Necesito que me despierten a mediodía

M: 我想订一个中午叫起服务?

A table for one, please

F: Une table pour une personne, s'il vous plaît

G: Einen Tisch für eine Person, bitte

S: Mesa para uno, por favor

M: 一位

What meat is this?

F: Quel type de viande est-ce?

G: Was für ein Fleisch is das?

S: ¿De qué es esta carne?

M: 这是什么肉?

Do you have any very cheap wine?

F: Avez-vous un vin vraiment bon marché?

G: Haben Sie irgendeinen sehr billigen Wein?

S: ¿Tienen algún vino barato?

M: 有没有便宜的酒

Same again, please

F: La même chose, s'il vous plaît

G: Das Gleiche nochmal bitte

S: Más de lo mismo, por favor

M: 再来一样的, 谢谢

I am sorry I spilt your drink

F: Excusez-moi d'avoir renversé votre boisson

G: Tut mir leid, dass ich Ihr Getränk verschüttet habe

S: Siento haberle tirado la bebida

M: 对不起我打翻了你的杯子

Anywhere. Just drive.

F: N'importe où. Vous n'avez qu'à conduire.

G: Egal wohin. Fahren Sie einfach.

S: A donde sea. Limítese a conducir.

M: 开车－去哪儿都好

Watch out for that truck!

F: Faites attention à ce poids lourd!

G: Vorsichtig, passen Sie auf den Lastwagen auf!

S: ¡Cuidado con ese camión!

M: 小心那货车!

I apologise, officer

F: Je m'excuse, monsieur l'agent

G: Es tut mir sehr leid, Herr Polizist

S: Le pido disculpas, agente

M: 对不起, 长官

I would like to reverse the charges

F: Veuillez demander à mon correspondant de payer la communication

G: Ich möchte bitte ein R-Gespräch anmelden

S: Me gustaría hacer una llamada a cobro revertido

M: 我想打一通受话人付费电话

I am locked in the toilet

F: Je me suis enfermé(e) dans les toilettes

G: Ich bin in der Toilette eingeschlossen

S: Estoy atrapado/atrapada en el baño

M: 我被困在厕所里

I have run out of petrol

F: Je n'ai plus de carburant

G: Mein Tank ist alle

S: Me he quedado sin gasolina

M: 我没汽油了

Police, fire and ambulance please

F: S'il vous plaît, envoyez la police, les pompiers et une ambulance

G: Polizei, Feuerwehr und Rettungswagen, bitte

S: Mande a la policía, los bomberos y una ambulancia, por favor

M: 我想叫警察, 消防车跟救护车

Not guilty

F: Non coupable

G: Nicht schuldig

S: Inocente

M: 不认罪

Can you stop talking?

F: Pouvez-vous arrêter de parler?

G: Können Sie bitte aufhören zu reden?

S: ¿Quiere hacer el favor de callarse?

M: 你可以闭嘴吗?

You might want to give it ten minutes

F: Je vous conseille d'attendre dix minutes

G: Ich würde da erstmal nicht reingehen

S: Quizás debería esperar diez minutos

M: 你要等它十分钟

I am tired

F: Je suis fatigué(e)

G: Ich bin müde

S: Estoy agotado/agotada

M: 我很累

It doesn't matter

F: Ne vous en faites pas

G: Ist total egal

S: No importa

M: 没关系了

Notable Deaths

Hank Williams
1 January 1953

Townes Van Zandt
1 January 1997

Amelia Earhart
5 January 1939

Paul Verlaine
8 January 1896

David Bowie
10 January 2016

James Joyce
13 January 1941

Shep
17 January 1987

Audrey Hepburn
20 January 1993

George Orwell
21 January 1950

Pete Seeger
27 January 2014

A.A. Milne
31 January 1956

Buddy Holly
3 February 1959

Alexander Pushkin
10 February 1837

Sylvia Plath
11 February 1963

Harper Lee
19 February 2016

Duncan Edwards
21 February 1958

Stan Laurel
23 February 1965

Stanley Matthews
23 February 2000

Donald Bradman
25 February 2001

Georges Perec
3 March 1982

Ivor Cutler
3 March 2006

John Candy
4 March 1994

Mark Linkous
6 March 2010

Karl Marx
14 March 1883

Chuck Berry
18 March 2017

Arthur C. Clarke
19 March 2008

Johann Wolfgang
von Goethe
22 March 1832

Johan Cruyff
24 March 2016

Garry Shandling
24 March 2016

Ian Dury
27 March 2000

Virginia Woolf
28 March 1941

Isaac Newton
31 March 1727

Jesse Owens
31 March 1980

Jesse James
3 April 1882

Kurt Cobain
5 April 1994

P.T. Barnum
7 April 1891

Frank Mars
8 April 1934

Pablo Picasso
8 April 1973

Edward Thomas
9 April 1917

Robert Edwards
10 April 2013

Franklin D. Roosevelt
12 April 1945

Thomas Andrews
15 April 1912

Greta Garbo
15 April 1990

Gabriel García Márquez
17 April 2014

Albert Einstein
18 April 1955

Anne Williams
18 April 2013

Charles Darwin
19 April 1882

Levon Helm
19 April 2012

Rubin Carter
20 April 2014

Prince Rogers Nelson
21 April 2016

Saul Bass
25 April 1996

Charley Patton
28 April 1934

Casey Jones
30 April 1900

Ayrton Senna
1 May 1994

Leonardo da Vinci
2 May 1519

Adam Yauch
4 May 2012

Henry David Thoreau
6 May 1862

Maurice Sendak
8 May 2012

Bob Marley
11 May 1981

Douglas Adams
11 May 2001

Gary Cooper
13 May 1961

Frank Sinatra
14 May 1998

June Carter Cash
15 May 2003

Ian Curtis
18 May 1980

Bonnie Parker
23 May 1934

Roger Moore
23 May 2017

Samuel Pepys
26 May 1703

Eric Morecambe
28 May 1984

John Noakes
28 May 2017

Christopher Marlowe
30 May 1593

Muhammad Ali
3 June 2016

David Markson
4 June 2010

Ray Bradbury
5 June 2012

Alan Turing
7 June 1954

Gerard Manley
Hopkins
8 June 1889

Hovis Presley
9 June 2005

Les Dawson
10 June 1993

Ella Fitzgerald
15 June 1996

James Gandolfini
19 June 2013

Niccolò Machiavelli
21 June 1527

Judy Garland
22 June 1969

Michael Jackson
25 June 2009

Tove Jansson
27 June 2001

Marlon Brando
1 July 2004

Ernest Hemingway
2 July 1961

Caroline Aherne
2 July 2016

Marie Curie
4 July 1934

Aneurin Bevan
6 July 1960

Billie Holiday
17 July 1959

John Coltrane
17 July 1967

Caravaggio
18 July 1610

Alan Lomax
19 July 2002

Amy Winehouse
23 July 2011

Notable Deaths (cont)

Samuel Taylor
Coleridge
25 July 1834

Vincent van Gogh
29 July 1890

Bobby Robson
31 July 2009

Cilla Black
1 August 2015

Joseph Conrad
3 August 1924

Lenny Bruce
3 August 1966

Marilyn Monroe
5 August 1962

Richard Burton
5 August 1984

Francis Ponge
6 August 1988

Tony Wilson
10 August 2007

Robin Williams
11 August 2014

William Blake
12 August 1827

Robert Johnson
16 August 1938

Federico García Lorca
19 August 1936

Groucho Marx
19 August 1977

Neil Armstrong
25 August 2012

Phyllis Pearsall
28 August 1996

Gene Wilder
29 August 2016

Seamus Heaney
30 August 2013

J. R. R. Tolkien
2 September 1973

Steve Irwin
4 September 2006

Roko Camaj
11 September 2001

Johnny Cash
12 September 2003

Grace Kelly
14 September 1982

Isambard Kingdom
Brunel
15 September 1859

Jimi Hendrix
18 September 1970

Virgil
21 September 19BC

Alan Fletcher
21 September 2006

Herman Melville
28 September 1891

Bill Shankly
29 September 1981

James Dean
30 September 1955

Woody Guthrie
3 October 1967

Peter Norman
3 October 2006

Janis Joplin
4 October 1970

Steve Jobs
5 October 2011

Jack Daniel
10 October 1911

Orson Welles
10 October 1985

Thomas Edison
18 October 1931

Jack Kerouac
21 October 1969

Rosa Parks
24 October 2005

Geoffrey Chaucer
25 October 1400

John Peel
25 October 2004

Lou Reed
27 October 2013

Ted Hughes
28 October 1998

Ezra Pound
1 November 1972

Ernst Gombrich
3 November 2001

Jacques Tati
5 November 1982

Patrick Moore
9 December 2012

Steve McQueen
7 November 1980

Otis Redding
10 December 1967

Leonard Cohen
7 November 2016

Richard Pryor
10 December 2005

John Milton
8 November 1674

Sam Cooke
11 December 1964

Arthur Rimbaud
10 November 1891

Walt Disney
15 December 1966

George Edwin Ellison
11 November 1918

Kirsty MacColl
18 December 2000

John F. Kennedy
22 November 1963

John Steinbeck
20 December 1968

Horace
27 November 8BC

Joe Strummer
22 December 2002

George Harrison
29 November 2001

William Thackeray
24 December 1863

Oscar Wilde
30 November 1900

Charlie Chaplin
25 December 1977

Odetta
2 December 2008

Dean Martin
25 December 1995

Frank Zappa
4 December 1993

George Michael
25 December 2016

Wolfgang Amadeus
Mozart
5 December 1791

Carrie Fisher
27 December 2016

Nelson Mandela
5 December 2013

Sam Peckinpah
28 December 1984

John Lennon
8 December 1980

Debbie Reynolds
28 December 2016

Bob Monkhouse
29 December 2003

On This Day

Leonardo da Vinci unsuccessfully tests flying machine
3 January 1496

First automobile hearse in use
15 January 1909

Black Monday
21 January 2008

Edvard Munch inspired to paint *The Scream*
22 January 1892

First canned beer sold
24 January 1935

Visitor falls down stairs in Fitzwilliam Museum, Cambridge, breaking three Qing Dynasty Chinese vases
25 January 2006

First electric dental drill
26 January 1875

Facebook founded
4 February 2004

First doughnut-making machine
6 February 1926

Longest traffic jam on record (109 miles)
16 February 1980

Opening and closing night of *Moose Murders*, worst-performing Broadway show in history
22 February 1983

Felix Hoffmann develops Aspirin
6 March 1899

David Marvin Jr sets human cannonball record
10 March 2011

Plastic wheelie bin invented
12 March 1968

Discovery of anti-matter
15 March 1962

World's first shopping mall opens in Michigan
22 March 1954

Werner Heisenberg publishes his Uncertainty Principle
23 March 1927

SOS distress signal developed
1 April 1905

The Beatles split up
10 April 1970

The most boring day in history according to one study
11 April 1954

Apple co-founder Ron Wayne sells 10% share for $800
12 April 1976

Patent filed for caller screening
8 May 1976

Patent filed for toilet brush
28 May 1933

First alarm clock with snooze feature
1 June 1959

Launch of the Doomsday Clock
2 June 1947

Museum of Failure opens in Sweden
7 June 2017

Domino's Pizza founded
10 June 1960

Donald Trump announces presidential run
16 June 2015

First International Potato Processing and Storage Convention
23 June 2009

Roy Sullivan struck by lightning for seventh time
25 June 1977

Release of *The Room*, directed by Tommy Wiseau, widely regarded as the worst film ever made
27 June 2003

Leopold Loyka, chauffeur to Archduke Ferdinand, makes wrong turn, encounters assassin and causes World War One
28 June 1914

999 emergency line launched in the UK
30 June 1937

Isaac Newton defines concept of inertia
5 July 1687

First lonely hearts ad
19 July 1695

Longest total solar eclipse of 21st century
22 July 2009

First self-checkout machine
5 August 1992

UK Bankruptcy Act
9 August 1869

32mm of rain falls in five minutes on Preston, UK
10 August 1893

Cricketer Don Bradman dismissed without score in final innings
14 August 1948

Potato chips invented
24 August 1853

World's largest turnip grown in USA
1 September 2004

Bon Accord lose 36–0 to Arbroath, the heaviest defeat in professional football
12 September 1885

First perforated toilet roll
15 September 1891

Battle of Karánsebes, in which the Austrian army accidentally fought itself and lost 10,000 men
21 September 1788

First edition of *Microwave for One* by Sonia Allison
23 September 1987

World record for most spoons balanced on face (31)
28 September 2013

Health and Safety at Work Act (UK)
1 October 1974

Fox News starts broadcasting
7 October 1996

World's largest cup of coffee (2,010 gallons) served in Las Vegas
15 October 2010

Black Monday
19 October 1987

First income tax laws introduced (USA)
22 October 1914

Beginning of the Great Depression
29 October 1929

M25 orbital road completed in UK
29 October 1986

First UK motorway services opens at Watford Gap
2 November 1959

Mary Celeste sets sail
7 November 1872

24-hour drinking laws introduced in UK
24 November 2005

John Michell predicts the existence of black holes
27 November 1783

Meteor strikes Ann Hodges, who survives with bruises
30 November 1954

Public launch of the Segway
3 December 2001

First Wetherspoon's pub opens
9 December 1979

Chris Rea's handwritten lyrics to 'Road to Hell' fail to sell at charity auction
15 December 2010

LinkedIn founded
28 December 2002

Personal SWOT Analysis

Strengths

Weaknesses

Opportunities

_____
_____
_____
_____

Threats

_____
_____
_____
_____
_____
_____
_____
_____
_____
_____
_____
_____
_____
_____
_____
_____
_____
_____

Tomorrow is yet another day

1
Hank Williams, d.1953
Townes Van Zandt, d.1997
New Year's Day

2

3
Leonardo da Vinci unsuccessfully tests flying machine, 1496

4

5
Amelia Earhart, d.1939

6

7

Crappe diem

8
Paul Verlaine, d.1896

9

10
David Bowie, d.2016

11

12

13
James Joyce, d.1941

14

If a tree falls in the woods and no one is there to hear it, does that remind you of your life?

15

First automobile hearse in use,
1909

16

17

Shep, d.1987

18

19

20

Audrey Hepburn, d.1993

21

George Orwell, d.1950
Black Monday, 2008

A journey of a thousand miles begins with a single step, followed by countless others, gradually merging into a relentless trudge

22
Edvard Munch inspired to paint 'The Scream', 1892

23

24
First canned beer sold, 1935

25

Burns Night
Visitor falls down stairs in Fitzwilliam Museum, Cambridge, breaking three Qing Dynasty Chinese vases, 2006

26
First electric dental drill, 1875

27
Pete Seeger, d.2014

28

If ignorance is bliss,
why are you so sad?

29

30

31
A.A. Milne, d.1956

1

2

3
Buddy Holly, d.1959

4
Facebook founded, 2004

Genius is 99% perspiration
and you've mastered that bit

5

6
First doughnut-making machine, 1926

7

8

9

10
Alexander Pushkin, d.1837

11
Sylvia Plath, d.1963

It takes two insufferable
people to tango

12

13

14
Valentine's Day

15

16
Longest traffic jam on record (109 miles), 1980

17

18

The glass is always half-empty
until you sigh and top it up

19
Harper Lee, d.2016

20

21
Duncan Edwards, d.1958

22
Opening and closing night of 'Moose Murders', worst-performing Broadway show in history, 1983

23
Stan Laurel, d.1965
Stanley Matthews, d.2000

24

25
Donald Bradman, d.2001

You can run but you are
better at hiding

26

27

28

29

1
St David's Day

2

3
Georges Perec, d.1982
Ivor Cutler, d.2006

Actions speak louder than you can handle right now

4
John Candy, d.1994

5

6
Felix Hoffmann develops Aspirin, 1899
Mark Linkous, d.2010

7

8
International Women's Day

9

10
David Marvin Jr sets human cannonball record, 2011

Good things come to those who don't deserve it

11

12
Plastic wheelie bin invented, 1968

13

14
Karl Marx, d.1883

15
Discovery of anti-matter, 1962

16

17
St Patrick's Day

Red sky at night, something's not right. Red sky in the morning, lingering feeling something terrible is going to happen

18
Chuck Berry, d.2017

19
Arthur C. Clarke, d.2008

20

21

22
Johann Wolfgang von Goethe, d.1832
World's first shopping mall opens in Michigan, 1954

23
Werner Heisenberg publishes his Uncertainty Principle, 1927

24
Johan Cruyff, d.2016
Garry Shandling, d.2016

Every action has a sarcastic and unhelpful reaction

25

26

27
Ian Dury, d.2000

28
Virginia Woolf, d.1941

29

30

31
Isaac Newton, d.1727
Jesse Owens, d.1980

A fool and his money are
text 10101 for the rest of this
sensational proverb

1

April Fool's Day
SOS distress signal developed, 1905

2

3
Jesse James, d.1882

4

5
Kurt Cobain, d.1994

6

7
P.T. Barnum, d.1891

You can't make an omelette
without breaking down in tears

8
Frank Mars, d.1934
Pablo Picasso, d.1973

9
Edward Thomas, d.1917

10
The Beatles split up, 1970
Robert Edwards, d.2013

11
The most boring day in history according to one study, 1954

12
Franklin D. Roosevelt, d.1945
Apple co-founder Ron Wayne sells 10% share for $800, 1976

13

14

No one likes a smart aleck but that's not the reason in your case

15
Thomas Andrews, d.1912
Greta Garbo, d.1990

16

17
Gabriel García Márquez, d.2014

18
Albert Einstein, d.1955
Anne Williams, d.2013

19
Charles Darwin, d.1882
Levon Helm, d.2012

20
Rubin Carter, d.2014

21
Prince Rogers Nelson, d.2016

You snooze, you drool

22

23
St George's Day

24

25
Saul Bass, d.1996

26

27

28
Charley Patton, d.1934

Don't get mad, get numb

29

30
Casey Jones, d.1900

1
Ayrton Senna, d.1994
International Workers' Day

2
Leonardo da Vinci, d.1519

3

4
Adam Yauch, d.2012

5

Another day, another net loss

6
Henry David Thoreau, d.1862

7

8
Patent filed for caller screening, 1976
Maurice Sendak, d.2012

9

10

11
Bob Marley, d.1981
Douglas Adams, d.2001

12

When the going gets tough, tough

13
Gary Cooper, d.1961

14
Frank Sinatra, d.1998

15
June Carter Cash, d.2003

16

17

18
Ian Curtis, d.1980

19

It's no use sobbing uncontrollably over spilt milk

20

21

22
World Goth Day

23
Bonnie Parker, d.1934
Roger Moore, d.2017

24

25

26
Samuel Pepys, d.1703

Uneasy come, uneasy go

27

28
Patent filed for toilet brush, 1933
Eric Morecambe, d.1984
John Noakes, d.2017

29

30
Christopher Marlowe, d.1593

31

1
First alarm clock with snooze feature, 1959

2
Launch of the Doomsday Clock, 1947

If you lose your job, you never have to work a day in your life

3
Muhammad Ali, d.2016

4
David Markson, d.2010

5
Ray Bradbury, d.2012

6

7
Alan Turing, d.1954
Museum of Failure opens in Sweden, 2017

8
Gerard Manley Hopkins, d.1889

9
Hovis Presley, d.2005

It ain't what you do, it's the grudging, half-hearted way you do it

10
Domino's Pizza founded, 1960
Les Dawson, d.1993

11

12

13

14

15
Ella Fitzgerald, d.1996

16
Donald Trump announces presidential run, 2015

Look before you leap
into the abyss

17

18

19
James Gandolfini, d.2013

20

21
Niccolò Machiavelli, d.1527

22
Judy Garland, d.1969

23
First International Potato Processing and Storage Convention, 2009

The darkest part of night is just before the dawn of another pointless day

24

25
Roy Sullivan struck by lightning for seventh time, 1977
Michael Jackson, d.2009

26

27
Tove Jansson, d.2001
Release of 'The Room', directed by Tommy Wiseau, widely regarded as the worst film ever made, 2003

28
Leopold Loyka, chauffeur to Archduke Ferdinand, makes wrong turn, encounters assassin and causes World War One, 1914

29

30
999 emergency line launched in the UK, 1937

Get hayfever while the sun shines

1

Marlon Brando, d.2004

2

Ernest Hemingway, d.1961
Caroline Aherne, d.2016

3

4

Marie Curie, d.1934
Independence Day (USA)

5

Isaac Newton defines concept of inertia, 1687

6

Aneurin Bevan, d.1960

7

Oui, je regrette beaucoup

8

9

10

11

12

13

14
Bastille Day (France)

Time is a great healer but you don't have much of it left

15

16

17
Billie Holiday, d.1959
John Coltrane, d.1967

18
Caravaggio, d.1610

19
First lonely hearts ad, 1695
Alan Lomax, d.2002

20

21

Every cloud has a silver lining around its heavy grey mass of imminent rain

22
Longest total solar eclipse of 21st century, 2009

23
Amy Winehouse, d.2011

24

25
Samuel Taylor Coleridge, d.1834

26

27

28

Two's company, three's a crowd,
as your parents like to say

29

Vincent van Gogh, d.1890

30

31

Bobby Robson, d.2009

1

Cilla Black, d.2015

2

3

Joseph Conrad, d.1924
Lenny Bruce, d.1966

4

No news is increasingly worrying

5
Marilyn Monroe, d.1962
Richard Burton, d.1984
First self-checkout machine, 1992

6
Francis Ponge, d.1988

7

8

9
UK Bankruptcy Act, 1869

10
32mm of rain falls in five minutes on Preston, UK, 1893
Tony Wilson, d.2007

11
Robin Williams, d.2014

Wake up and smell the super-strength cider

12
William Blake, d.1827

13

14
Cricketer Don Bradman dismissed without score in final innings, 1948

15

16
Robert Johnson, d.1938

17

18

A friend is just a stranger you haven't fallen out with yet

19
Federico García Lorca, d.1936
Groucho Marx, d.1977

20

21

22

23

24
Potato chips invented, 1853

25
Neil Armstrong, d.2012

You make your own
incredibly bad luck

26

27

28
Phyllis Pearsall, d.1996

29
Gene Wilder, d.2016

30
Seamus Heaney, d.2013

31

1
World's largest turnip grown in USA, 2004

There's no 'I' in 'team' but there is a 'u' in 'failure'

2
J. R. R. Tolkien, d.1973

3

4
Steve Irwin, d.2006

5

6

7

8

There are plenty more fish in the vast, implacable ocean

9

10

11
Roko Camaj, d.2001

12
Bon Accord lose 36–0 to Arbroath, the heaviest defeat in professional football, 1885
Johnny Cash, d.2003

13

14
Grace Kelly, d.1982

15
Isambard Kingdom Brunel, d.1859
First perforated toilet roll, 1891

Losers gonna lose

16

17

18
Jimi Hendrix, d.1970

19

20

21
Virgil, d.19BC
Battle of Karánsebes, in which the Austrian army accidentally fought itself and lost
10,000 men, 1788
Alan Fletcher, d.2006

22

You might as well have another cake and eat it

23

First edition of 'Microwave for One' by Sonia Allison, 1987

24

25

26

27

28

Herman Melville, d.1891
World record for most spoons balanced on face (31), 2013

29

Bill Shankly, d.1981

The best defence is complete emotional withdrawal

30
James Dean, d.1955

1
Health and Safety at Work Act (UK), 1974

2

3
Woody Guthrie, d.1967
Peter Norman, d.2006

4
Janis Joplin, d.1970

5
Steve Jobs, d.2011

6

What doesn't kill you makes
you wish it had

7

Fox News starts broadcasting, 1996

8

9

10

Jack Daniel, d. 1911
Orson Welles, d.1985

11

12

Hispanic Day

13

Never do today what you might
as well put off until tomorrow

14

15

World's largest cup of coffee (2,010 gallons) served in Las Vegas, 2010

16

17

18

Thomas Edison, d.1931

19

Black Monday, 1987

20

Forewarned is anxious and fearful

21
Jack Kerouac, d.1969

22
First income tax laws introduced (USA), 1914

23

24
Rosa Parks, d.2005

25
Geoffrey Chaucer, d.1400
John Peel, d.2004

26

27
Lou Reed, d.2013

Everything happens for a
terrifyingly random reason

28
Ted Hughes, d.1998

29
Beginning of the Great Depression, 1929
M25 orbital road completed in UK, 1986

30

31
Hallowe'en

1
Ezra Pound, d.1972

2
First UK motorway services opens at Watford Gap, 1959

3
Ernst Gombrich, d.2001

Burn that bridge when you come to it

4

5
Jacques Tati, d.1982
Bonfire Night

6

7
'Mary Celeste' sets sail, 1872
Steve McQueen, d.1980
Leonard Cohen, d.2016

8
John Milton, d.1674

9

10
Arthur Rimbaud, d.1891

Despair springs eternal

11

George Edwin Ellison, d.1918

12

13

14

15

16

17

If at first you don't succeed,
get used to it

18

19

20

21

22
John F. Kennedy, d.1963

23

24
24-hour drinking laws introduced in UK, 2005

When one door closes another
one opens in your face

25

26

27

Horace, d.8BC
John Michell predicts the existence of black holes, 1783

28

29

George Harrison, d.2001

30

Oscar Wilde, d.1900
Meteor strikes Ann Hodges, who survives with bruises, 1954
St Andrew's Day

1

Worse things happen at sea
but this is bad as land-based
events go

2
Odetta, d.2008

3
Public launch of the Segway, 2001

4
Frank Zappa, d.1993

5
Wolfgang Amadeus Mozart, d.1791
Nelson Mandela, d.2013

6

7

8
John Lennon, d.1980

When you wish upon a star, bear in mind it may already be dead and you're wishing on the dying rays that have made their way, millions of years later, across the dark, indifferent void

9
First Wetherspoon's pub opens, 1979
Patrick Moore, d.2012

10
Otis Redding, d.1967
Richard Pryor, d.2005

11
Sam Cooke, d.1964

12

13

14

15
Walt Disney, d.1966
Chris Rea's handwritten lyrics to 'Road to Hell' fail to sell at charity auction, 2010

Hip, hip... replacement!

16

17

18
Kirsty MacColl, d.2000

19

20
John Steinbeck, d.1968

21

22
Joe Strummer, d.2002

You'd better watch out, you'd better not cry, you'd better not pout, I'm telling you why – your extended family is coming to visit

23

24
William Thackeray, d.1863

25
Charlie Chaplin, d.1977
Dean Martin, d.1995
George Michael, d.2016
Christmas Day

26
Boxing Day

27
Carrie Fisher, d.2016

28
Sam Peckinpah, d.1984
LinkedIn founded, 2002
Debbie Reynolds, d.2016

29
Bob Monkhouse, d.2003

Same shit, different year

30

31

1
Hank Williams, d.1953
Townes Van Zandt, d.1997
New Year's Day

2

3
Leonardo da Vinci unsuccessfully tests flying machine, 1496

4

5
Amelia Earhart, d.1939

The Gaping Void Ahead
Next Year Planner

January

February

March

April

May

June

The Gaping Void Ahead
Next Year Planner

July

August

September

October

November

December

People Who Never Call

Name

Address

Telephone

Mobile

Email

Name

Address

Telephone

Mobile

Email

Name

Address

Telephone

Mobile

Email

Name

Address

Telephone

Mobile

Email

Name

Address

Telephone

Mobile

Email

Name

Address

Telephone

Mobile

Email

People You Owe Money

Name   Amount

Address

Telephone

Mobile

Email

Name   Amount

Address

Telephone

Mobile

Email

Name   Amount

Address

Telephone

Mobile

Email

Name

Amount

Address

Telephone

Mobile

Email

Name

Amount

Address

Telephone

Mobile

Email

Name

Amount

Address

Telephone

Mobile

Email

Imaginary Friends

Name

Address

Telephone

Mobile

Email

Name

Address

Telephone

Mobile

Email

Name

Address

Telephone

Mobile

Email

Name

Address

Telephone

Mobile

Email

Name

Address

Telephone

Mobile

Email

Name

Address

Telephone

Mobile

Email

Real Enemies

Name

Address

Telephone

Mobile

Email

Name

Address

Telephone

Mobile

Email

Name

Address

Telephone

Mobile

Email

Name

Address

Telephone

Mobile

Email

Name

Address

Telephone

Mobile

Email

Name

Address

Telephone

Mobile

Email

Notes Toward A Dull Novel

Notes Toward A Laboured Poem

Notes Toward An Unnecessary Verse Drama

Notes Toward An
Abandoned Screenplay

Notes Toward An
Incomplete Haiku

Notes Toward A Tweet
Everyone Will Ignore

Notes From A Boring Meeting

Notes From An Urgent Performance Appraisal

Ideas You'll Never Follow Up

Ideas You'll Discard In The Morning

Laughable To Do List

Apology Notes

Dear
I'm incredibly sorry for

From

Dear
I'm incredibly sorry for

From

Dear
I'm incredibly sorry for

From

Dear

I'm incredibly sorry for

From

Dear

I'm incredibly sorry for

From

Dear

I'm incredibly sorry for

From

Passive-Aggressive Notes

Dear _____

Just so you know, _____

_____

_____

_____

_____

Have a great day. _____

From _____

Dear _____

Just so you know, _____

_____

_____

_____

_____

Have a great day. _____

From _____

Dear _____

Just so you know, _____

_____

_____

_____

_____

Have a great day. _____

From _____

Dear

Just so you know,

Have a great day.

From

Dear

Just so you know,

Have a great day.

From

Dear

Just so you know,

Have a great day.

From

Notes To Self

Replies To Self

Pointless Doodles

More Pointless Doodles

Page Unintentionally Left Blank

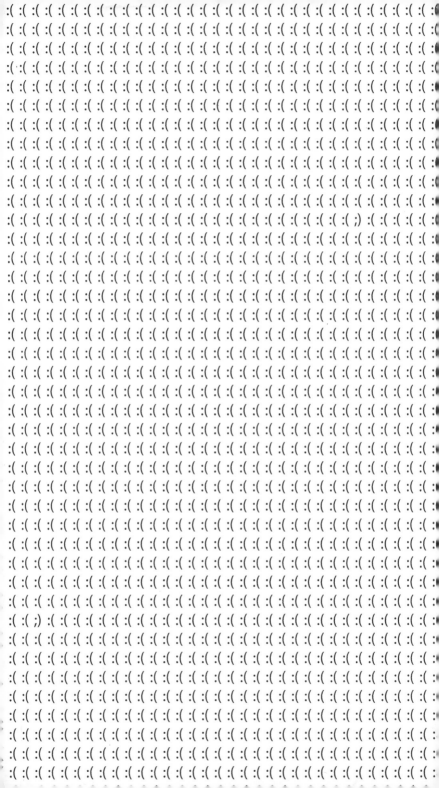